The Responsible me !

By
Ray E. Robinson Jr.
and
Dr. Shanetta Weatherspoon

Illustration by
Ananta Mohanta

RW
LEADERSHIP SERVICES
TRANSFORMING PEOPLE, BUSINESSES & COMMUNITIES INTO LEADERS

Momma reminds Ray, "Lil Ray,
it is time for practice.
Do not forget your water or your bat!"

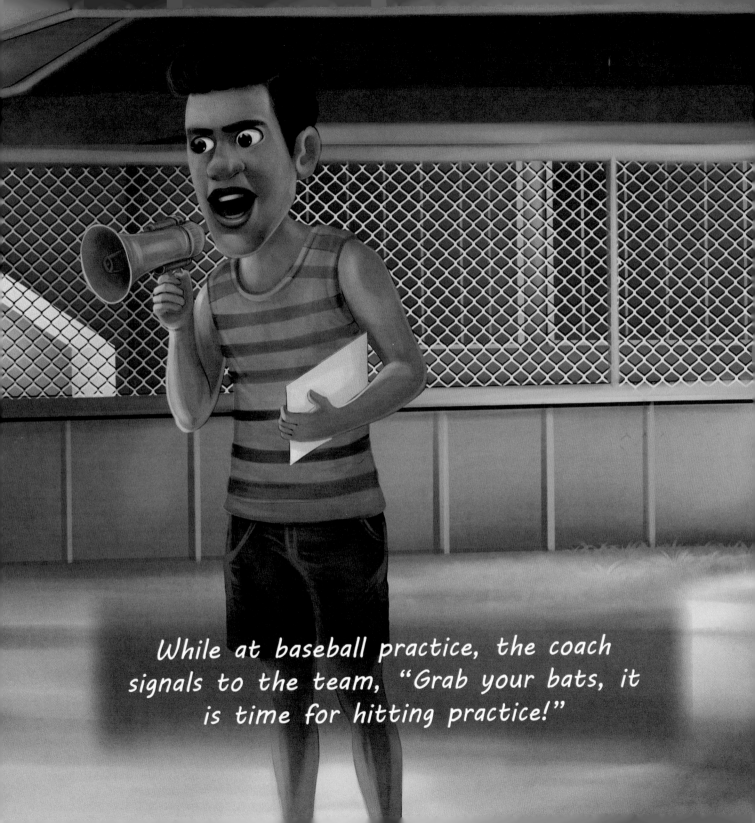

While at baseball practice, the coach signals to the team, "Grab your bats, it is time for hitting practice!"

The coach yells, "Lil Ray forgot his bat, so the entire team is running laps for practice! Maybe next time, he will be more responsible."

Lil Ray inquires, "Momma, what does responsible mean?"

Momma explains, "Well son, being responsible is caring enough for the things that you are required to do and doing them without me or anyone else telling you or reminding you."

She continues, "For example, when you do your chores without me telling you, you are being responsible."

Lil Ray asks, "Momma, how do you feel when I am responsible?"

His Momma proclaims, "Son, I feel very proud of you when you are responsible."

Momma clarifies, "When you are responsible, it makes your life and the lives of the people who depend on you, much easier."

Momma adds, "For example, imagine if you had remembered your bat and water today. Your entire team would not have had to run all those laps. Remembering your bat and water is an example of being responsible."

She continues, "Son, it is important for you to remember that when you are irresponsible, it not only affects you, but it also affects the people around you."

Lil Ray proclaims with certainty, "I am going to show everyone the responsible me!"

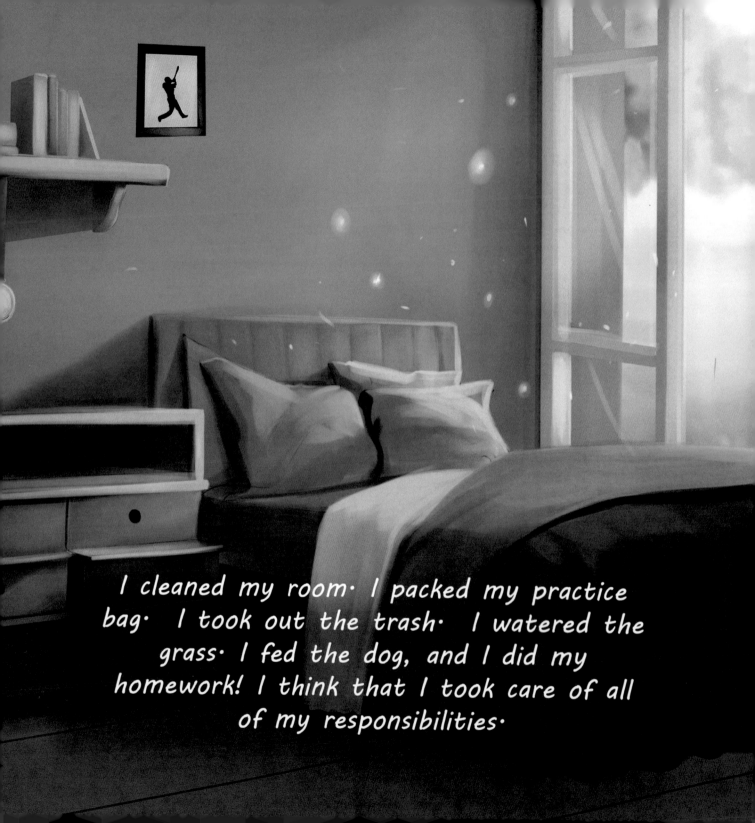

I cleaned my room. I packed my practice bag. I took out the trash. I watered the grass. I fed the dog, and I did my homework! I think that I took care of all of my responsibilities.

Lil Ray proclaims with certainty, "I am going to show everyone the responsible me!"

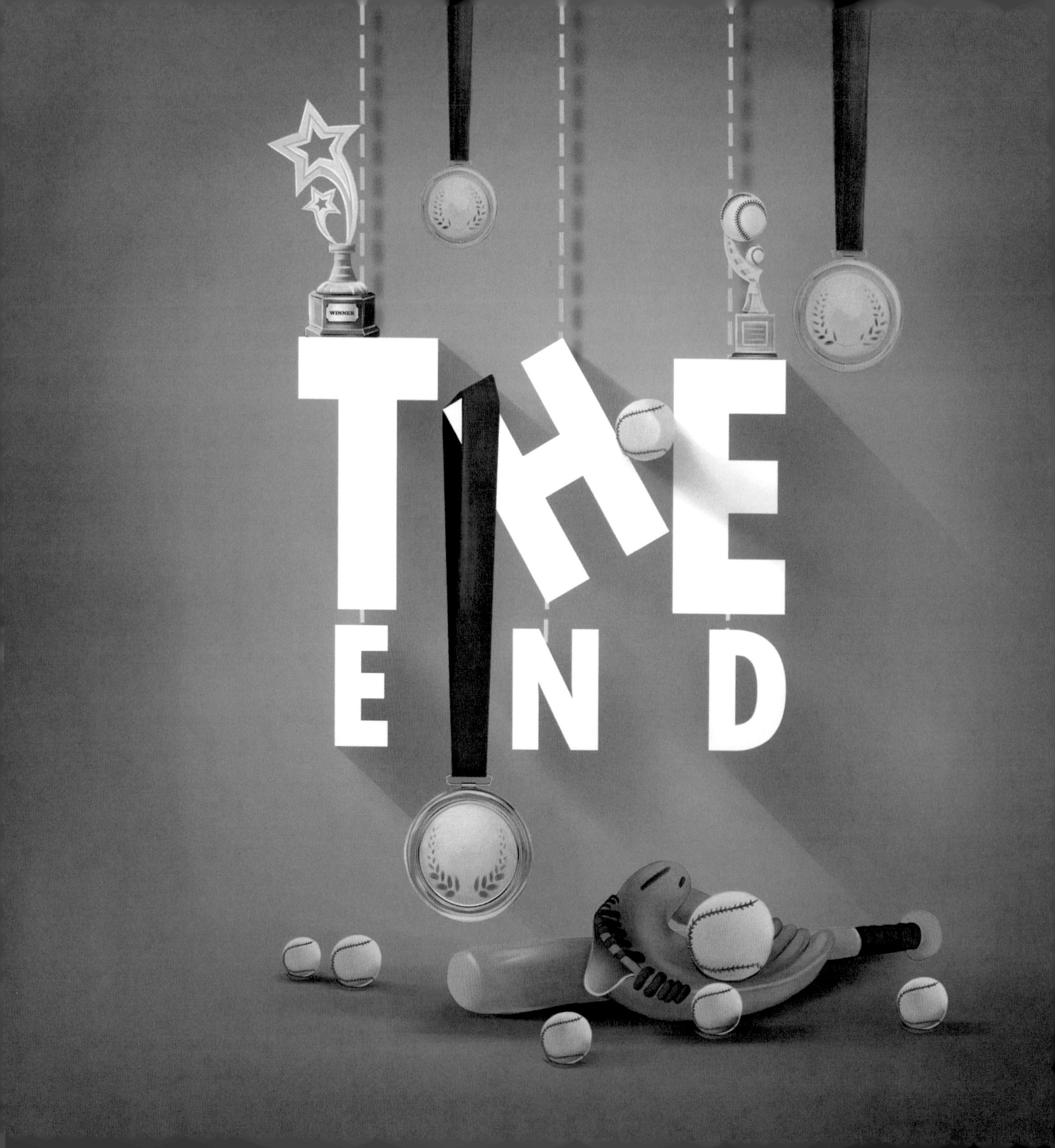
WINNER
THE
END

LEADERSHIP SERVICES

TRANSFORMING PEOPLE, BUSINESSES & COMMUNITIES INTO **LEADERS**

Meet the Founders/Authors

Ray E. Robinson II is a founder of R&W Leadership Services, LLC; Instagram: RW_Leaders. Ray is also a junior at St. John Bosco High School, where he is a member of their Entrepreneur Track, focusing on leadership. He plays both baseball and basketball and looks forward to going to college in Fall 2023. Currently, he is dual-enrolled in college courses including Psychology and Philosophy. He enjoys spending time with his family, dog-Ares, and assisting his great-grandmother in his free time. His long-term professional goal is to become an attorney. This children's book collection is important to Ray, because he hopes that his personal journey for answers will inspire others along their way.

Meet the Founders/Authors

Nailah C. Robinson is a founder of R&W Leadership Services, LLC. Nailah is also a sophomore at the University of California, Berkeley (CAL) with the intention to major in Molecular Cell Biology with an emphasis in Genetics. She enjoys spending time with her family and assisting with the management of the family business; Instagram: RW_Leaders. Her long-term professional goal is to become a medical doctor (MD). After she completes her undergraduate career at CAL, she plans to take the MCAT in order to be eligible for medical school. After medical school, a personal goal of hers is to tackle the documented disparities in the medical field that are disproportionately affecting minority communities. This children's book collection is important to Nailah, because she hopes that her personal journey for truth and self-love will inspire others along their way.

Meet the Founders/Authors

Dr. Shanetta Weatherspoon is principal consultant and CEO of R&W Leadership Services, LLC and the proud mother of both Nailah and Ray. She has over fifteen years of leadership experience in the non-profit and higher education industries. Dr. Weatherspoon presents at conferences on topics including; organizational development, leadership, diversity, and youth/family empowerment.

Currently, she is the Executive Director of Pepperdine's Foster Grandparent Program. She is also a dedicated educator; having served as an adjunct faculty member with academic institutions including Pepperdine GSEP, California State University, Long Beach, the Paul Merage School of Business (UCI), Mount Saint Mary's University and the University of Pittsburgh. Her favorite class to teach is the Psychology of Prejudice & Discrimination. Dr. Weatherspoon holds a B.A. in Psychology, a MPA, a MBA with a specialization in HRM, a Doctorate in Organizational Leadership from Pepperdine Graduate School of Education & Psychology and is a certified Senior Professional of Human Resources (SPHR). Her personal motto is "Achievement Requires Commitment."

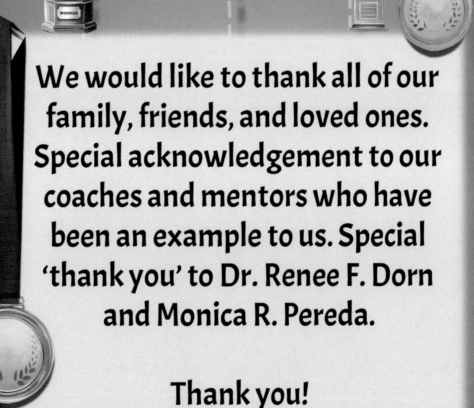

We would like to thank all of our family, friends, and loved ones. Special acknowledgement to our coaches and mentors who have been an example to us. Special 'thank you' to Dr. Renee F. Dorn and Monica R. Pereda.

Thank you!

Made in the USA
Las Vegas, NV
20 October 2023

79391268R00026